My Book

David
from
Grandmother Watt

Christmas 1969.

That Happy Feeling of Thank You

of

Story by ⚘ ⚘ ⚘
PETER STILLMAN

Illustrations by
JUDY STANG ⚘

THE C. R. GIBSON COMPANY
NORWALK, CONNECTICUT

Do you know that there are
two kinds of "Thank you"?
One is the out-loud kind
(which you often say with a smile) —
THANK YOU
It is a short, polite way of saying —
You have been very kind to me.

Have you *said* "Thank you" today?

To Mother or Daddy for finding that toy
you thought you had lost?

To a friend for letting you try
his two-wheeler?

Or even to little sister for helping
you pick up after play?

If you have said "Thank you"
at least once today
(without being reminded) —
You know all there is to know
about the out-loud kind.

The other kind of "Thank you"
　　has almost no sound at all.
It whispers deep inside you
　　when you are very very happy
In a way it is like the out-loud
　　　　THANK YOU
It is another way of saying,
You have been very kind to me.
In a way it is quite different —
　　This kind of "Thank you" is
　　the one that only God hears.

Has God heard your "Thank you" today?

"Thank you" comes at break of day,
Creeping into your room
In sunlight and good-mornings.

"Thank you" is for hands cupped
To hold small, important things —
    A pet frog, cool water,
    A secret that needs sharing.

"Thank you" is a ride on a merry-go-round
When the world is a *whiz* of colors
And the wind and music tickle your ears.

"Thank you" is to know a friend
Who will stretch out on the warm grass
And pretend along with you
That the whole world is upside-down.

"Thank you" is seeing the first—
the very first—
robin in your neighborhood

And having him build his nest
in *your* tree.

The world is full of favorite things —
Some as tiny as a lady-bug,
Some as big as a thunderstorm.

What are your favorite things?

The big parade that swings through town
With marching feet,
Booming drums, prancing horses,
And shiny fire engines?

Feeding peanuts to elephants at the zoo?

Or to squirrels in your back yard?

A rainbow that bends in the sky
after summer rain?

Lightning bugs blinking
On a warm summer night?

The sound of Daddy's car in the drive?

"Thank you" is for favorite things.

And "Thank you" is for growing up, too—

For being brave enough
To tell the truth—
Even when it would be easier not to.

For *knowing,* suddenly, that
If one and one make two,
Then two and two *must* make four.

"Thank you" is for not being afraid
   of darkness
   or being alone.

And, for sleepy boys and girls
    after evening prayer,
"Thank you" is for a fluffy dream
    Of falling stars
    And a white pony—

And knowing, even though
you are fast asleep,
That a loving God
is watching over you.

Thank you for the
world so sweet,
Thank you for the
food we eat,
Thank you for the
birds that sing,
Thank you, God,
for everything